Time Machine Research Project: Genghis Khan

Alphabet Publishing

Taylor Sapp

Contents

Before You Read

1. Would you rather live 50 years in the future or 50 years in the past

2. Do you think we will be able to travel in time in the future?

3. If time travel were real, what period in the past would you go back to? Why?

4. What person in history do you think is most misunderstood?

Time Travel Machine Research Project

Everyone said Professor Atkins' research class was rewarding, but time-consuming. That's because we would actually go back in time! Atkins' class was the first history class in the world to use new time travel technology. What an opportunity!

It was also the hardest class in the world to get into. It was only open to PhD students. Professor Atkins had to approve every student. I was very nervous sitting in Professor Atkins' tiny office. I looked around at the wall-to-wall papers and books. His elbows sat on books about Ancient Egypt and the Great Wall of China.

"So what topic do you want to study, Li Ying?" the professor asked me.

"You can call me Joy." My father was born in China and my mother had European roots. Even though my legal name was Li Ying Chen, I had blue eyes and medium-brown hair. In the US, it confused people. I preferred to go by my English name, Joy.

I continued. "I'm planning to research Genghis Khan. Most people think that Genghis Khan was cruel. That he loved war. Others say that he was actually very progressive for the time. I want to explore the real Genghis Khan."

"OK," Atkins said, "This is a good start but you need to be more specific. Can you think of one particular issue that is important to you?"

"Actually, I am interested in his attitudes to women. In a time, where women had little power, I believe the Khan was different. I think he respected women's opinions. Many records say his wives acted as advisors. And we know after his death, his sons' wives were very powerful. Where did his sons learn respect for women?" I went on in greater detail as Atkins nodded.

At the end of my presentation, Professor Atkins leaned back in his chair. He looked serious.

"You know, this is an opportunity few get. Thousands have fought just to sit where you are right now and give their proposals. Yours is by no means the best I've heard. I'm not sure that you can prove that Genghis Khan believed in women's rights. That being said, I'm impressed by your background. Your academic record is very impressive. I'm also very interested in your family history as a first-generation immigrant from Taiwan with European and Asian roots. As you know, Genghis Khan's empire covered much of Asia and Europe. He conquered many different peoples. His advisors came from all over his empire. Your appearance, both Asian and European, will serve you well. Congratulations, you are in my class!"

On the morning of the first class, I was in such a rush that I didn't even notice the tall, blond man holding open the door to the history building.

"Are you in Atkin's research class?" He had a light Swedish accent.

He was so impressive I could barely say yes in response.

We both walked slowly to the classroom. He asked me about my project, which I described in great detail.

As we reached the classroom, I realized he hadn't a chance to explain his.

"Don't worry, we can talk more later!" he said.

I certainly hoped so!

There were nine other students in Atkin's class-room. I didn't know any of them. We were each asked to introduce ourselves and our subject of research.

The first to speak was a very pretty, dark-haired girl: "Jabra Slate, Cleopatra era of Egyptian history."

A shy-looking guy said, "Dogi Sato, Meiji era, Japan"

"Sven Kurden, Viking era, Northern Europe." The tall blond man smiled at me as he said it.

The group kept going around until finally, it ended with me. "Joy Chen, Mongolian history, 13th Century CE."

Professor Atkins smiled.

"A very impressive group. I'm looking forward to your research. Today we will discuss the details of time travel. I have been running time travel research projects for the last 5 years without any major accidents and I plan to continue that record. So please listen carefully as I explain."

He picked up a small box and handed out a thin, clear rubber bracelet with computer chips and wires inside it to each student.

"This will be the key to your travel and safety. These bracelets have many uses. They also make time travel possible. When you want to go home, press this part. The time machine uses your bracelet to locate you and move you through time. Do not lose it or you will be stuck in the past, maybe forever!

"You will pair up and travel together. This is so you have someone to help you in your research. It is very important for safety. If one of you gets lost or your bracelet breaks, the other one can get help.

"You will take turns helping each other with your research projects. I expect you to take both projects seriously. As for your partners ..."

I crossed my fingers hoping for Sven. He seemed nice and he was very good looking. I did not want Jabra to be my partner, just because I don't know about Egypt. I definitely didn't want to partner with Dogi. He seemed way too shy and awkward.

"Brooke and John, Romi and Jamal, Emma and Karl, Sven and Jabra, Dogi and Joy."

Dogi's eyes met mine for a second. Then he looked away, embarrassed. I hadn't even spoken with him yet and I was already annoyed.

So it was me and Dogi, the awkward student from Japan.

Professor Atkins demonstrated the uses of the bracelet. Besides time travel, it also created acted as a universal translator.

"Any language that enters the invisible field generated by your bracelet will be translated to English. The computer knows all the languages in the world and in history. Anything you say will be translated into the correct language for the person you are talking to.

"Do you have any questions?"

"Why did you pair us all with another gender?" Dogi asked.

Atkins turned and spoke to the group.

"This has come up in the past. The main reason is for the safety of the women. For example, Joy is travelling to Karakorum in the Mongol Empire in the 13th century. If she were alone without a man, she'd be an easy target. She could be stolen and made a slave, at the very least. You wouldn't want to happen, would you?

"Let me remind all of my history students, women's rights are very limited throughout history, and still are today many would argue. For better or worse, a male companion will protect the women and let them conduct their research.

"It does help the man, too. In some periods a man who wasn't married would be seen as strange. So having a woman accompany you will help people take you seriously!"

Dogi said ok, but it sounded weak. I couldn't believe I had to share the experience of a lifetime with him. He was short and not particularly handsome. Worst of all was his shyness.

OK, I didn't have to like him. However, I worried about our safety. I planned to test how Genghis Khan reacted to a strong woman. I thought Genghis Khan respect me. However, I could be wrong. In that case, Dogi would need to act like a strong man, Maybe he would have to fight!

I thought about Sven and Jabra. That lucky girl! If I was traveling with him, I knew I'd have nothing to worry about. Now I'd have to protect Dogi. I didn't even know if he could tie his shoelaces.

— *ele* —

Two days later, it was time to go. We met in the lab where the time-machine was prepared and ready. The machine filled a whole room. There was a doorway full of blue light in the middle.

Dogi and I were both dressed fully in clothes from the period. I was dressed like a Mongolian Royal Princess with a beautiful Kazakh-style red dress and head wear.

Dogi was dressed in the uniform of the *Kheshig* or Mongolian Royal Guard: Thick layers of armor, a helmet, a shield, bow and arrow, and a Japanese katana sword.

"You idiot," I said.

"What?" Dogi asked.

"Your sword is Japanese. Genghis Khan never conquered Japan. The Royal Guard wouldn't have a Japanese sword!"

"But it's my favorite sword. I use it in roleplaying games all the time," Dogi said smiling. He drew the sword and waved it around like a little kid playing.

I screamed at him, "Hey, that thing is sharp. Careful!"

My words surprised him. He looked down and tried to put the sword back. His hands were shaking so it took him a few tries.

Atkins was standing by the doorway, watching us with a slight smile. "You both look great. Now step through the blue light and you'll go back to 1220."

Dogi and I closed our eyes and walked through the door.

A second later, we were in a large open field. It was sunny. It looked like a lot of places in the modern day US.

But this place was different, as the approaching men on horses indicated. About 20 men wearing *deels*, traditional Mongolian robes, approached us, swords drawn. But we were prepared with both a speech and letter about our transfer to Genghis Khan's Royal Guard, as ordered by Jochi, one of his own sons.

"I am Muqali, the leader of this group. How did you get here without horses?"

Dogi took the lead, as would be customary. "We had horses, but the enemy attacked us. Everyone was killed or ran away. We were in real trouble until you appeared."

We had invented this story so that we could meet Genghis Khan. Dogi told the soldiers the rest of our story, "The attack was not a coincidence. We have important information for the Khan. That is why the enemy is trying to stop us."

I ran my hand over my bracelet. I wouldn't hesitate to use it to escape if things turned sour. I knew how easily violence came in this period.

These tough warriors would have no problem killing us if they didn't believe us.

The leader looked at us with great suspicion. But then he pointed at one of his men. "Double up with Ghosen and give them your horse."

He pointed back at us. "You can ride together on his horse."

"I'm not sure if we can ride at all," I whispered as a joke.

To my surprise, Dogi slapped me in the face!

And even more surprisingly, all of the men laughed!

"She is a good woman, but she has no control over what comes out of her mouth!" Dogi said.

Part of me wanted to slap him right back, but the other part was impressed. I didn't think he'd had it in him!

When we were finally alone, I slapped Dogi right back in the face as hard as I could. He yelled in surprise more than pain.

Before he could respond, I spoke. "Before you say anything, you did the right thing. So let's call it even?"

"Just keep letting me do the talking," Dogi said.

"You know this is my project, right? I can't test what Genghis thinks about women if I am silent. I will speak and we will see how he reacts." I couldn't believe how bossy he was already getting!

"We don't know what Khan is really like. You think he respects women, but what if you're wrong?"

"If I believed that, I wouldn't be here!"

There he was: the great Genghis Khan. He was the most successful military conqueror in history. He ruled over many people. He was also a great warrior who killed many people. His army did terrible things. However, he advanced the Mongol Empire. All religions were treated equally. There was no conflict between tribes.

The Mongol Empire had a postal service, paper money, and laws that were fair to everyone.

Of course, Genghis Khan was a human being too. He wore thick clothes and his beard hid his face. I couldn't see him well except for his intense eyes. This was a man to be spoken to very carefully. Did he also have progressive ideas?

Muqali was whispering into Khan's ear. He was pointing at us in a way that made me very nervous.

"Great Khan. We have come from the West with a message," Dogi began, but I stepped in front and interrupted. There was no sense waiting.

"It is my message, so I want to tell it." Khan's royal guards and the entire room gasped, and I saw Dogi's hand immediately go for his bracelet. If I was wrong, we'd need to make a quick escape.

Everyone in the room looked shocked. But I kept my gaze on the Khan. His expression never changed or showed any emotion. Finally, he laughed.

"Is this your wife?" he asked Dogi.

"Yes, Great Khan," Dogi answered.

"Too bad. She would make a fine wife for me," he laughed.

Genghis Khan wasn't talking to me. However, he wasn't angry at me. What would he do next?

I decided to speak again, "Thank you for the kind words, Great Khan. But we are here with important information."

The Khan looked at Dogi, then slowly turned his head to me. He pointed at me with his hand, palm facing up, as if to say "Go on'. The message was clear. He preferred to talk to a man. However, he would listen to me.

"Great Khan. In the West, our warriors fight well. We take many prisoners. Some of the prisoners are women. Your law says the women should be respected. However, some of your soldiers are not respectful. They treat the female prisoners badly."

"Can you tell me why you care about women prisoners?" The Khan looked amused.

"Your Highness, the law applies to everyone equally, does it not?" I said.

"Are you serious?" he asked. "Why should we respect enemies?"

"If prisoners are treated badly, continued expansion will be difficult. The enemy will fight to the death. They will not want to be captured. It will be harder to conquer them. Furthermore, your people will have no respect for you."

"You make a good point," Genghis said. "I have said it many times, the sword is the most necessary, but not the only, step. You are right to bring this to my attention." He spoke without emotion, "I am finished with this matter. I will see that the necessary orders are delivered."

It was a huge victory. Genghis Khan had listened to the advice of a woman. He cared how women were treated. It was hard to believe. I only believed it myself because it happened to me.

Genghis Khan turned back to Dogi. He asked him to stay to discuss some of the details while I was led back to our yurt, a round Mongolian tent. When Dogi returned, he looked uncomfortable. He assured me that the Khan had not changed her mind.

———ℓℓℓ———

I was woken up late in the night by a middle-aged woman. She took me aside to a private spot to chat.

"The Khan is quite taken with you. He says he hasn't met any woman like you before. He wants to buy you from your husband."

"Why are you telling me?"

"Because I know what will happen. If your husband says no, the Khan will respect this decision, but his own men will not. They will kill your husband and bring you to the Khan as a gift. Your husband must agree."

I returned to the tent and work up Dogi.

"We have to go!" Dogi said after I explained. He looked at me carefully. "Why do you still look so calm?"

I shook my head. "We can go back as soon as we want to, but I want a final meeting with the Khan! I didn't even really get to talk to him!"

"We're in a dangerous spot here. There are people around who will kill me and make you a slave. But maybe you can tell Genghis Khan the truth."

I wondered about that. It hadn't occurred to me, but Dogi might be right ... again!

I decided to go meet the Khan alone. I was led to his sleeping yurt, which made me feel very nervous. Inside, the yurt was covered with animal skins on the walls and floor. He was seated on the fur of a Siberian tiger.

"Sit," he commanded.

I sat nervously.

"Be calm," he said. "I only want to talk."

"Pardon me, Great Khan, but I was told you were looking for something more."

"It is true, you are a fine woman. I am the king. I can take anything I want. But your husband spoke very well of your union and I respect that. I want to talk about something else with you."

I nodded, feeling relieved. "Please go on."

"I know you are not who you seem. You do not belong to my tribe. Muqali, the leader of the group that found you, thinks you must be spies."

"We are not spies," I said quickly.

"Muqali says I must torture you for information. What do you say to that?"

My mouth opened but nothing came out. I was starting to panic. The Khan picked a sword up from the floor.

"This blade has tasted the blood of many liars!"

What should I do? Would he even understand the truth? I tried desperately to think of what to stay, but I remained frozen.

And then, my surprise, the Khan laughed.

"I don't know who you are, but you are no threat. Spies know what to say when they are

19

captured. I suggest you go back to your husband and leave my camp. It is safer if you go before morning."

I gazed at his face and his cold, but strangely understanding, eyes. I couldn't understand why he let me go. Suddenly, without thinking, I told him about the time machine and my mission. He listened, stroking his chin. After I finished, he spoke, "You come from the future? An impossible story. You would be dead before you finished if you told such a thing to Muqali. You are looking to judge the way I treat women?"

"I know that women and men do a lot of the same work in your land. I know about your great respect for marriage, how you teach both men and women to defend their home ..." I then explained to him about women's rights in the 20th century.

He listened carefully. "Hoelun, my mother, a woman, was the strongest and fiercest person I have ever known. She was a survivor and one of my most trusted advisors, along with my wife."

I remembered a Chinese proverb that the Khan had apparently liked: "Women hold up half the sky."

He nodded his head. "I like that saying. I think I will say it at my son's, Tolui, wedding in three days."

Uh-oh. Had I changed history?

"Now I suggest you be on your way," he finished.

When I got back to our yurt, Dogi was dressed and ready to go. Having the face-to-face with Khan had been enough. Maybe I couldn't prove my thesis that Genghis Khan was a feminist and believed women were equal to me. However, he had been very respectful of women.

"Ok, time to go home." Dogi and I both pressed on our bracelets just as Professor Atkins had taught us.

Nothing happened. We tried a few more times.

"Why isn't it working?" Dogi asked.

"Is it because we're inside? Atkins did say it works better outside."

We both went outside and bumped into a group of five of the Khan's guards. Their leader was Muqali.

"Going somewhere?" he asked.

"Yes, it was getting a bit hot in there," I said.

"I am an expert at protecting the Great Khan, and your behavior gives me pause." Muqali was short but dangerous looking. I knew we were in serious danger.

"We will go back to sleep," Dogi said as calmly as he could. He opened the flap to his yurt, but two guards quickly grabbed him.

"I think it is time for you to leave," Muqali said to Dogi. Then he looked at me. "But not you. You will stay and become one of the Khan's wives."

"I'd rather leave with my husband." It was very strange to talk like that about Dogi.

"I don't think you will like where he is going," Muqali smiled cruelly.

Dogi was trying to get his bracelet to work with no results. I tried my best not to panic, thinking of how we could get out of this.

"Muqali, what are you up to?" A woman emerged from the shadows. She was the woman who had woken me up!

"Borte! What are you doing here?" Muqali stared at her. Borte was the Khan's first wife, a tough woman. According to some historians, she had been a true equal to the Khan. It certainly was looking that way.

Borte spoke in a loud clear voice. "Remove your men immediately. Did you not forget? They have a task to complete in the morning."

"Don't be a fool, Borte. Their task is a lie and this man is a spy! I will take care of him. As for the woman, she will make a good wife for the Khan once properly trained."

"You would ignore the Khan's orders? Do you know the penalty for this?"

Muqali laughed. "I only see a foolish woman here. You test my patience. Perhaps the three

of you should all 'leave' and never come back."
He looked at the guards who grabbed me and
moved toward Borte.

Borte looked at him. "Khan sent me, Muqali.
If any of us disappear, you will lose your head!
Now enough of this. Go back to your yurt immediately, Otherwise, I will tell the Khan about
your crime tonight!"

Muqali stared at the three of us for the longest
minute of my life. Then he sighed and raised his
hands. "Let them go," he told the guards.

"Thank you," I said to Borte. There were so
many questions I wanted to ask her, as a strong
woman living in such a different time, but there
was no time.

She said, "I know three things: You are not who
you say you are. You are no danger to us. Muqali
is dangerous."

I wanted to warn her; Genghis Khan would die
in battle and some historians think Muqali killed
him. I couldn't change history though.

Instead, I simply said, "You wouldn't believe the truth if I told you."

Soon after, Dogi and I were outside the camp in an open field. Our bracelets were blinking softly which meant it was time to come back!

"Are you ready for one more trip?" Dogi asked. "Don't forget, I still have to do my research too!"

I asked him eagerly. "So where are we headed next?"

Glossary

advisor: a person who gives advice to a person, particularly a leader

armor: something worn over clothes to protect from harm in battle, usually made of metal or leather

commanded: gave an order

conquered: took control of, particularly through war

conqueror: a person who wins a war against other people and takes control of their land

customary: usual, expected behavior in a situation

feminist: a person who believes women should have the same rights as men

gasped: breathed out air quickly in surprise or excitement

intense: (*here*) full of emotion and personal strength

palm: the inner part of the hand from the wrist to the bottom of the fingers

PhD: the highest graduate degree you can get, also called a doctorate

proverb: a saying that gives advice or wisdom

respectful: full of consideration for other people's feelings

robes: a long piece of clothing that covers most of your body and opens in the front

shield: a large flat piece of wood or metal held in the hand for protection in battles

torture: to hurt someone so that they will give you information or to punish them

warrior: a fighter, a person involved in war

yurt: a round cloth tent used by Mongolians and Central Asians

After You Read

1. Why does Joy speak to Professor Atkins in the first scene?

2. What is unusual about Professor Atkins' class?

3. What is Joy's research question? How will she answer it?

4. What does Joy think about Sven?

5. What does she think about Dogi?

6. What historical figure do Dogi and Joy meet?

7. What is their purpose in meeting that

person?

8. How does her meeting go? Is she successful or not?

9. What did Joy do in her second meeting? Do you think she made a good choice or not?

10. Who is Muqlai and what does he plot to do to her?

11. Who is Borte? How does Borte help Joy?

12. Do you think Joy proves her hypothesis? Why or why not?

13. How does Joy and Dogi's relationship change?

- Do they like each other in the beginning of the story?

- How do their feelings change at the end?

Writing

1. What happens on Dogi's research project?

- Where and when do they go?

- What theory do they test?

- What happens?

2. Design your own historical research project. Think of a question about history you want to learn about. It could be something you want to know about a person, place, or event.

- Where and to what time do you have to go to answer that question?

- Who do you have to speak to?

- What do you have to observe?

- What evidence will answer your question or prove you right or wrong?

- What challenges might you face?

3. Now write a story about your adventure in time!

More Readers

AlphabetPublish.com/Book-Category/
Graded-Reader

CPSIA information can be obtained
at www.ICGtesting.com
Printed in the USA
LVHW051823290623
751158LV00004B/434

9 781956 159400